PLAYLADDERS

by
Hannah Mortimer

A QEd Publication

Published in 2000

ISBN 1 898873 09 7

Published by QEd, The Rom Building, Eastern Avenue, Lichfield, Staffs. WS13 6RN

Printed in the United Kingdom by Stowes (Stoke-on-Trent).

Contents

How to use Playladders

The Playladders were designed for mainstream nursery teachers and early years educators who have children with special educational needs in their care. They are a method of **assessing** and **recording** what the child can do, and provide **ideas** on how to help the child move on to the next 'step'.

Playladders are based on the following assumptions:

1) Early years staff do not need to have specialist knowledge in order to help children with special educational needs in their nurseries – they are already specialists in how young children learn.

2) Children with special educational needs are, by and large, no different from other children whom the teacher will have already helped. They will usually play in the same ways, though may need to be **shown** how to play by an adult, supported in their play, and given opportunities to access the toys and activities.

3) Early years staff are busy people and may not have the time to withdraw children for individual assessment and help; instead, any system they use to do this must fit closely with what already goes on in the nursery/classroom.

4) Early years teachers' time is most valuably spent playing alongside the children, thereby helping those children with special educational needs to increase their repertoire of play activities, to **think** about what they are doing and, thus, to learn.

5) Children with special educational needs may need to learn 'one step at a time', learning first to do simple activities and later to combine these into more complex tasks.

Whilst you are playing alongside the child, use each Playladder to record what the child is doing at a particular activity on a particular date. At the same time, you will see ideas on how to help the child increase his or her repertoire of play, choosing an activity at a level to be a suitable 'next step' for the child. Step 1 is at the bottom of the ladder to the left of each activity. The activities get progressively more difficult as one moves up each step towards the top of the ladder. A comments box is also available to add any further information you may wish to include about the child's progress.

Enter a ✓ if the child has demonstrated a particular behaviour, and a ✗ if the behaviour is a well-established part of his or her repertoire.

Do not be 'bound' by the Playladders – adapt, modify, supplement them to suit the children in your care. A number of blank Playladders can be found at the end of this booklet to enable you to design your own. If you need more information or more specialist advice on how to help a particular child, you may need to contact a support service in your area.

Playladders

Nursery area | LARGE SPACE

Play activity | CLIMBING FRAME

Comments

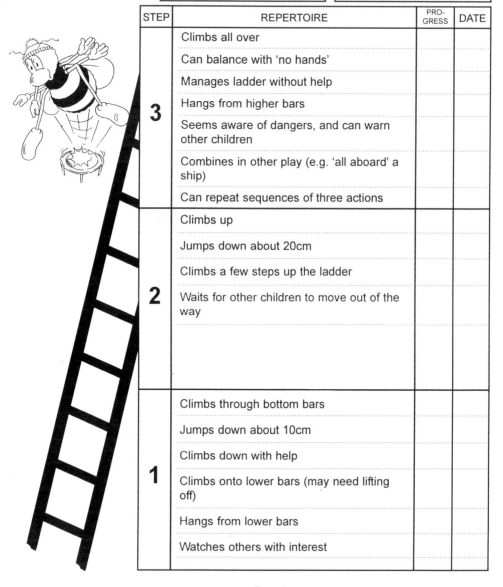

STEP	REPERTOIRE	PRO-GRESS	DATE
3	Climbs all over		
	Can balance with 'no hands'		
	Manages ladder without help		
	Hangs from higher bars		
	Seems aware of dangers, and can warn other children		
	Combines in other play (e.g. 'all aboard' a ship)		
	Can repeat sequences of three actions		
2	Climbs up		
	Jumps down about 20cm		
	Climbs a few steps up the ladder		
	Waits for other children to move out of the way		
1	Climbs through bottom bars		
	Jumps down about 10cm		
	Climbs down with help		
	Climbs onto lower bars (may need lifting off)		
	Hangs from lower bars		
	Watches others with interest		

Playladders

Nursery area | LARGE SPACE

Play activity | TRICYCLE/CAR

Comments

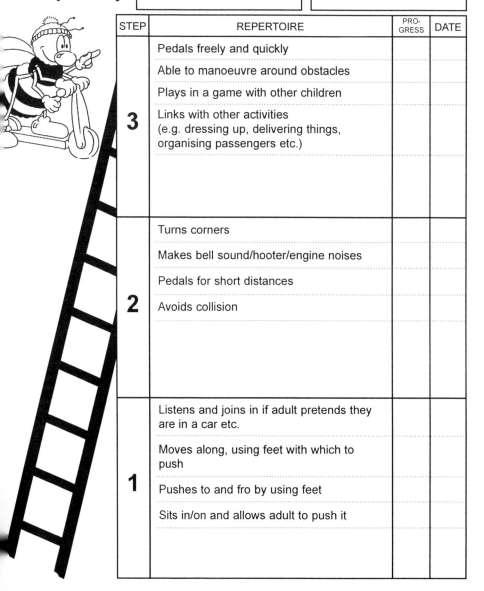

STEP	REPERTOIRE	PRO-GRESS	DATE
3	Pedals freely and quickly		
	Able to manoeuvre around obstacles		
	Plays in a game with other children		
	Links with other activities (e.g. dressing up, delivering things, organising passengers etc.)		
2	Turns corners		
	Makes bell sound/hooter/engine noises		
	Pedals for short distances		
	Avoids collision		
1	Listens and joins in if adult pretends they are in a car etc.		
	Moves along, using feet with which to push		
	Pushes to and fro by using feet		
	Sits in/on and allows adult to push it		

Playladders

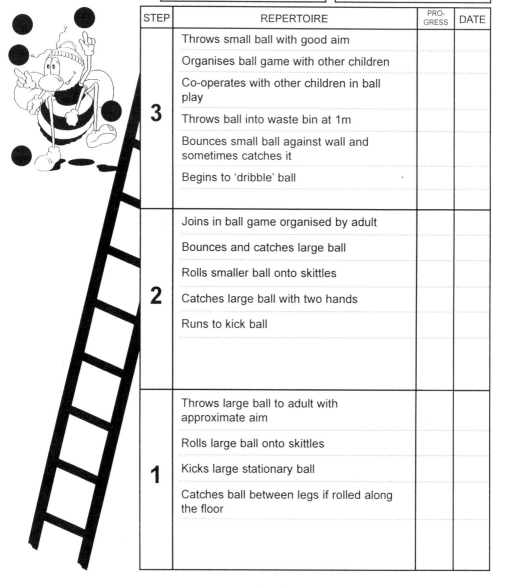

Nursery area | LARGE SPACE

Play activity | BALL PLAY

Comments

STEP	REPERTOIRE	PRO-GRESS	DATE
3	Throws small ball with good aim		
	Organises ball game with other children		
	Co-operates with other children in ball play		
	Throws ball into waste bin at 1m		
	Bounces small ball against wall and sometimes catches it		
	Begins to 'dribble' ball		
2	Joins in ball game organised by adult		
	Bounces and catches large ball		
	Rolls smaller ball onto skittles		
	Catches large ball with two hands		
	Runs to kick ball		
1	Throws large ball to adult with approximate aim		
	Rolls large ball onto skittles		
	Kicks large stationary ball		
	Catches ball between legs if rolled along the floor		

Playladders

Nursery area | LARGE SPACE

Play activity | FLOOR GAMES

Comments

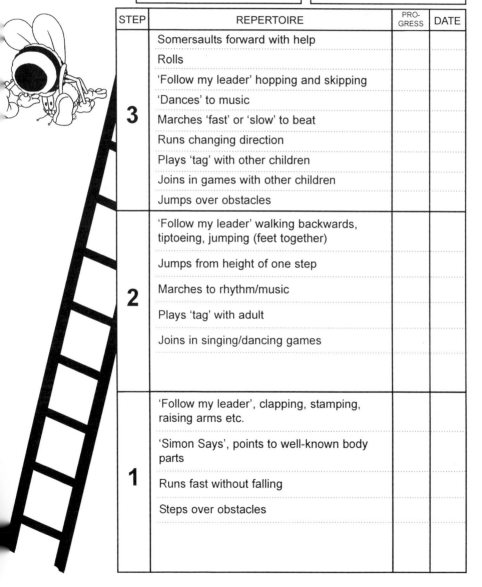

STEP	REPERTOIRE	PRO-GRESS	DATE
3	Somersaults forward with help		
	Rolls		
	'Follow my leader' hopping and skipping		
	'Dances' to music		
	Marches 'fast' or 'slow' to beat		
	Runs changing direction		
	Plays 'tag' with other children		
	Joins in games with other children		
	Jumps over obstacles		
2	'Follow my leader' walking backwards, tiptoeing, jumping (feet together)		
	Jumps from height of one step		
	Marches to rhythm/music		
	Plays 'tag' with adult		
	Joins in singing/dancing games		
1	'Follow my leader', clapping, stamping, raising arms etc.		
	'Simon Says', points to well-known body parts		
	Runs fast without falling		
	Steps over obstacles		

Playladders

Nursery area	TABLE GAMES	Comments
Play activity	DRAWING/COLOURING	

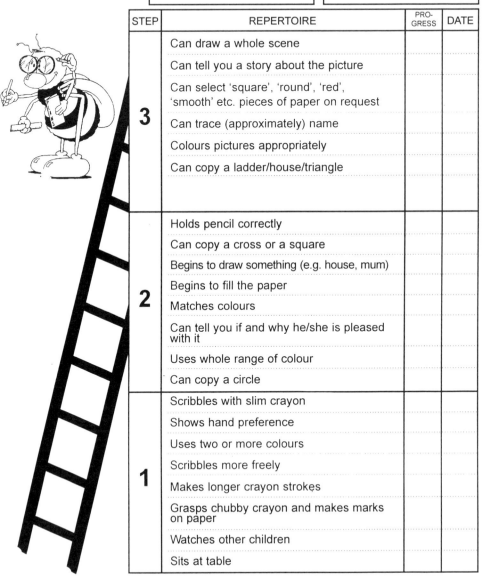

STEP	REPERTOIRE	PRO-GRESS	DATE
3	Can draw a whole scene		
	Can tell you a story about the picture		
	Can select 'square', 'round', 'red', 'smooth' etc. pieces of paper on request		
	Can trace (approximately) name		
	Colours pictures appropriately		
	Can copy a ladder/house/triangle		
2	Holds pencil correctly		
	Can copy a cross or a square		
	Begins to draw something (e.g. house, mum)		
	Begins to fill the paper		
	Matches colours		
	Can tell you if and why he/she is pleased with it		
	Uses whole range of colour		
	Can copy a circle		
1	Scribbles with slim crayon		
	Shows hand preference		
	Uses two or more colours		
	Scribbles more freely		
	Makes longer crayon strokes		
	Grasps chubby crayon and makes marks on paper		
	Watches other children		
	Sits at table		

Playladders

Nursery area	TABLE GAMES	Comments
Play activity	CO-ORDINATION TOYS	

STEP	REPERTOIRE	PRO-GRESS	DATE
3	Copies finger rhymes		
	Plays successfully with miniature toys/animals in doll's house/zoo		
	Makes successful bridge with bricks		
	Models Lego/Sticklebricks etc. with purpose		
	Threads small beads		
	Moves fingers independently on electronic keyboard/piano		
2	Sorts black/white miniature objects/small buttons/beads		
	Stacks 8–9 small cubes		
	Threads large beads onto thread with stiffened end		
	Fits together Lego/Sticklebricks etc. into simple construction		
1	Builds a tower using 5–6 small cubes		
	Threads cotton reels onto mounted knitting needle		
	Threads pop-up cone tree		
	Pulls apart Lego/Sticklebricks etc.		
	Stacks beakers (with help on order of size)		
	Fits in formboard shapes (with help on matching)		

Playladders

Nursery area | TABLE GAMES

Play activity | PUZZLES

Comments

STEP	REPERTOIRE	PRO-GRESS	DATE
3	Can select own puzzle and complete it without help		
	Can sort pieces into separate puzzles		
	Able to look at picture detail when selecting next piece		
	Can complete orientation/reversal formboards		
2	Puts together parts of 3-D shape to make a whole (e.g. half eggs)		
	Puts together familiar simple jigsaw		
	Begins to look for shape of next piece		
	Begins to look for colour of next piece		
	Can grade size (e.g. penguin formboard)		
	Can complete simple formboards		
	Puts together 3-piece jigsaw		
1	Can match simple shapes		
	Completes 2-piece jigsaw (e.g. picture cut in half)		
	Can complete simple 3-piece formboard ○ ▢ △		
	Can fit circular shape into circular space		
	Can remove pieces from simple formboard		

Playladders

Nursery area | TABLE GAMES

Play activity | EARLY NUMBER

Comments

STEP	REPERTOIRE	PRO-GRESS	DATE
3	Can pace out a room		
	Counts to 20 if asked		
	Counts out up to 10 objects as part of useful task		
	Tells you which pile of counters has 'more' and proves it		
	Begins to charge 'appropriate' prices in nursery shop e.g. 2p for big bun, 1p for little bun		
	Exchanges 1p or 2p in nursery shop		
2	Joins in more complex number rhymes (to 10)		
	Counts to 10 if asked		
	Counts out 5 objects		
	Passes round cups (one each)		
	Puts straws into bottles		
	Exchanges 'money' in nursery shop		
	Sorts colours/shapes/animals		
1	Can pass round 3 cups to 3 dolls		
	Counts to 5 if asked		
	Counts with adult to 3		
	Helps adult count over 3 objects		
	Joins in familiar number rhymes (to 5)		

Playladders

Nursery area	LET'S PRETEND	Comments	
Play activity	HOME CORNER		

STEP	REPERTOIRE	PRO-GRESS	DATE
3	Combines play with other areas of the nursery (e.g. uses art work to decorate, makes model cooker etc.)		
	Joins in fully with other children in imaginative play using own imaginative ideas		
2	Collects pans for pan cupboard, food for pantry etc.		
	Joins in a game directed by other children		
	Puts doll to bed and covers it up		
	Dresses and undresses doll		
	Plays on own with more complicated activity – moving from one part of home corner to another (e.g. making breakfast)		
	Plays on own – simple activity (e.g. ironing, holding imaginary telephone conversation)		
1	Puts things in and takes things out of kitchen cupboards		
	Helps to tidy up		
	Brings adult a 'cup of tea' if asked		
	Holds and cuddles doll		
	Kisses doll if adult suggests it		
	Replies to adults on telephone		
	Speaks into telephone held by adult		

Playladders

Nursery area | LET'S PRETEND

Play activity | DRESSING UP

Comments

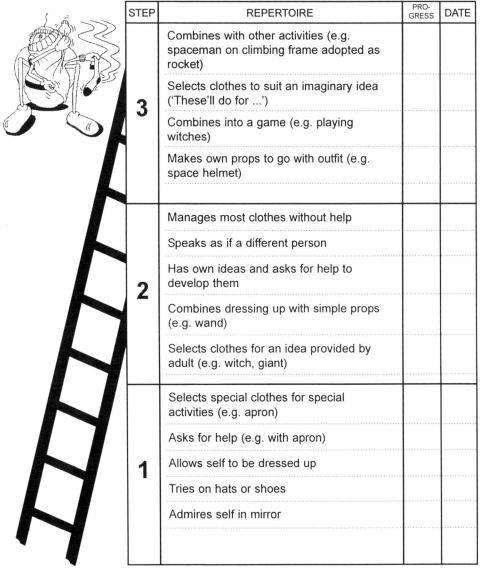

STEP	REPERTOIRE	PRO-GRESS	DATE
3	Combines with other activities (e.g. spaceman on climbing frame adopted as rocket)		
	Selects clothes to suit an imaginary idea ('These'll do for ...')		
	Combines into a game (e.g. playing witches)		
	Makes own props to go with outfit (e.g. space helmet)		
2	Manages most clothes without help		
	Speaks as if a different person		
	Has own ideas and asks for help to develop them		
	Combines dressing up with simple props (e.g. wand)		
	Selects clothes for an idea provided by adult (e.g. witch, giant)		
1	Selects special clothes for special activities (e.g. apron)		
	Asks for help (e.g. with apron)		
	Allows self to be dressed up		
	Tries on hats or shoes		
	Admires self in mirror		

Playladders

Nursery area | ALL THE TIME

Play activity | TALKING

Comments

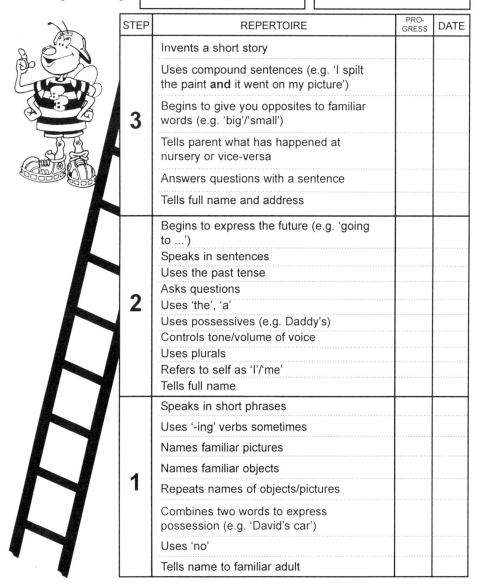

STEP	REPERTOIRE	PRO-GRESS	DATE
3	Invents a short story		
	Uses compound sentences (e.g. 'I spilt the paint **and** it went on my picture')		
	Begins to give you opposites to familiar words (e.g. 'big'/'small')		
	Tells parent what has happened at nursery or vice-versa		
	Answers questions with a sentence		
	Tells full name and address		
2	Begins to express the future (e.g. 'going to ...')		
	Speaks in sentences		
	Uses the past tense		
	Asks questions		
	Uses 'the', 'a'		
	Uses possessives (e.g. Daddy's)		
	Controls tone/volume of voice		
	Uses plurals		
	Refers to self as 'I'/'me'		
	Tells full name		
1	Speaks in short phrases		
	Uses '-ing' verbs sometimes		
	Names familiar pictures		
	Names familiar objects		
	Repeats names of objects/pictures		
	Combines two words to express possession (e.g. 'David's car')		
	Uses 'no'		
	Tells name to familiar adult		

Playladders

Nursery area	ALL THE TIME	Comments	
Play activity	UNDERSTANDING		

STEP	REPERTOIRE	PRO-GRESS	DATE
3	Listens to short stories and answers simple questions on it		
	Can suggest **why** someone might be doing something		
	Tells adult if it is morning or afternoon		
	Finds 'heavy', 'shiny', 'fast' objects (i.e. more abstract concepts)		
2	Follows more complicated instructions (e.g. '... **then** ...')		
	Finds 'big', 'red' (simple colours), 'your ...' objects to request		
	Finds 'top' or 'bottom'		
	'long' or 'short'		
	'high' or 'low'		
1	Carries out simple directions (e.g. 'give me the ball')		
	Points to familiar picture if asked		
	Points to familiar object if asked		
	Shows through actions that the use of an object is understood (e.g. hammer)		
	Finds 'big' one		
	Understands 'no'		

Playladders

Nursery area	ALL THE TIME	Comments
Play activity	HELPING MYSELF	

STEP	REPERTOIRE	PRO-GRESS	DATE
3	Serves drinks to other children		
	Puts on coat and fastens up		
	Manages shoes independently		
	Tidies up independently		
	Comes in from outside to use toilet		
	Selects appropriate things to buy for picnic		
	Butters bread for picnics		
	Cleans up splashes etc.		
	Helps to sweep up		
	Goes on simple message with friend into another room		
2	Pours own drink		
	Sucks from straw		
	Manages toilet independently		
	Regulates own water at sink		
	Hangs up coat		
	Puts toys away in right places if reminded		
	Helps with simple commands (e.g. 'can you find the ...?')		
	Clears up accidental spills with help		
	Hands over money in shop if buying picnic food		
	Helps to spread sandwiches for picnics		
	Hands round picnic food		
1	Puts on shoes (not fastenings)		
	Puts on socks		
	Puts toys away if helped		
	Manages open cup		
	Takes cup to sink		
	Lets adult know when toilet is needed		
	Goes to toilet if reminded and with help		
	Helps to pull down clothes at toilet		
	Takes off coat if unfastened		
	Finds own coat		
	Finds front of clothing		
	Washes hands if adult regulates water		

Playladders

Nursery area	ALL THE TIME
Play activity	GETTING ON

Comments

STEP	REPERTOIRE	PRO-GRESS	DATE
3	Plays co-operatively with other children		
	Offers/initiates help to adult		
	Offers/initiates help to other child		
	'Negotiates' a game with other children		
	Can apologise		
	Can say 'please' and 'thank you'		
	Follows instructions given to group (e.g. 'put your coats on' or 'line up together')		
2	Approaches other children		
	Speaks to other children if spoken to		
	Accepts toys from other children		
	Begins to take turns		
	Accepts direction from adult		
	Can apologise with help		
1	Watches other children		
	Begins to play alongside other children		
	Speaks or asserts self if 'taken over' by other children		
	Joins in game with adult		
	Answers questions from adult with single words		
	Plays alongside adult, so long as you are close by		
	Allows familiar adult to be close by and talking softly		
	Accepts comfort from familiar adult		

Playladders

| Nursery area | BOOK CORNER |
| Play activity | |

Comments

STEP	REPERTOIRE	PRO-GRESS	DATE
3	Follows through idea of story onto other activities		
	Chooses a book and tells adult about it		
	Can discuss the story and its associated ideas		
	Listens, as part of a group, to story with occasional pictures		
	Pretends to 'read' own story		
	Can tell adult a story just from looking at the pictures		
	Can suggest what happens next		
2	Chooses a book and tells adult why		
	Interrupts with associated idea (e.g. 'I've got a cat too!')		
	Anticipates familiar repeated words or pictures		
	Listens to longer story		
	Shows pleasure/surprise/other emotions		
	Selects book for adult		
1	Names familiar pictures		
	Sits looking at book		
	Turns pages one at a time		
	Listens to very short story with pictures		
	Finds a familiar book to request		
	Points to familiar named pictures		
	Looks at more complicated pictures		
	Holds picture book right way up		
	Looks at pictures – one object per page		

Playladders

Nursery area | MUSIC CORNER

Play activity

Comments

STEP	REPERTOIRE	PRO-GRESS	DATE
3	Claps rhythm of name		
	Marches to rhythm of music		
	Uses percussion rhythmically		
	Joins in a song in tune		
	Can sing/dance/play 'loud', 'soft', 'fast', 'slow'		
	Can make a musical instrument		
	Can produce sound effects to a story		
	Selects familiar music		
	Sings songs/jingles learned outside nursery		
2	Plays musical bumps with good listening		
	Knows how to make appropriate sounds from most nursery instruments		
	Begins to control voice		
	Claps a steady rhythm with help		
	Joins in familiar songs (not necessarily tunefully)		
1	Experiments with different musical instruments		
	Joins in some words or actions of songs		
	Enjoys rhymes/songs and tries to join in		
	Claps hands to request		
	Will pat tambourine as adult holds it		
	Watches/listens with interest		
	'Lalas' to tune though not necessarily **in** tune		

Playladders

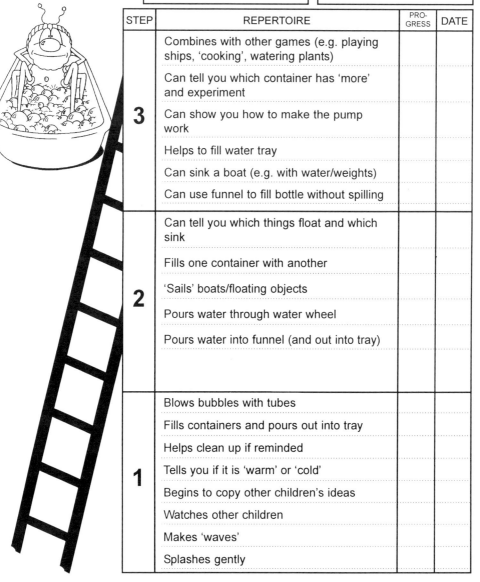

	Nursery area	MESSY	Comments
	Play activity	WATER PLAY	

STEP	REPERTOIRE	PRO-GRESS	DATE
3	Combines with other games (e.g. playing ships, 'cooking', watering plants)		
	Can tell you which container has 'more' and experiment		
	Can show you how to make the pump work		
	Helps to fill water tray		
	Can sink a boat (e.g. with water/weights)		
	Can use funnel to fill bottle without spilling		
2	Can tell you which things float and which sink		
	Fills one container with another		
	'Sails' boats/floating objects		
	Pours water through water wheel		
	Pours water into funnel (and out into tray)		
1	Blows bubbles with tubes		
	Fills containers and pours out into tray		
	Helps clean up if reminded		
	Tells you if it is 'warm' or 'cold'		
	Begins to copy other children's ideas		
	Watches other children		
	Makes 'waves'		
	Splashes gently		

Playladders

Nursery area MESSY

Play activity CLAY/DOH

Comments

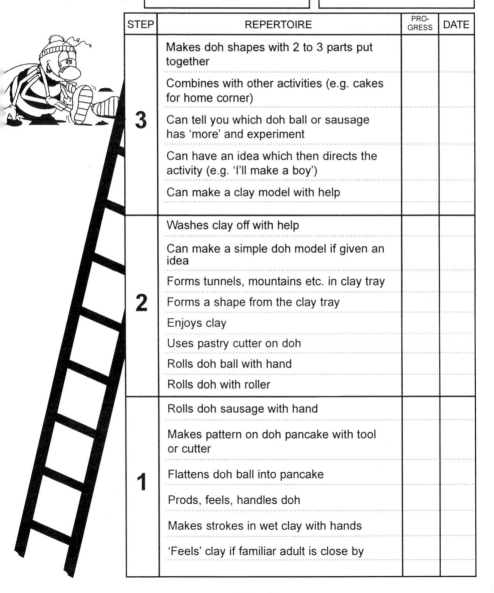

STEP	REPERTOIRE	PRO-GRESS	DATE
3	Makes doh shapes with 2 to 3 parts put together		
	Combines with other activities (e.g. cakes for home corner)		
	Can tell you which doh ball or sausage has 'more' and experiment		
	Can have an idea which then directs the activity (e.g. 'I'll make a boy')		
	Can make a clay model with help		
2	Washes clay off with help		
	Can make a simple doh model if given an idea		
	Forms tunnels, mountains etc. in clay tray		
	Forms a shape from the clay tray		
	Enjoys clay		
	Uses pastry cutter on doh		
	Rolls doh ball with hand		
	Rolls doh with roller		
1	Rolls doh sausage with hand		
	Makes pattern on doh pancake with tool or cutter		
	Flattens doh ball into pancake		
	Prods, feels, handles doh		
	Makes strokes in wet clay with hands		
	'Feels' clay if familiar adult is close by		

Playladders

Nursery area | MESSY

Play activity | PAINTING

Comments

STEP	REPERTOIRE	PRO-GRESS	DATE
3	Expresses more complicated idea (e.g. 'Me **with** my dog')		
	Manages to keep colours separate if trying to		
	Talks about picture		
	Uses wide range of colours		
	Helps to mix poster paints		
	Hangs up finished picture to dry		
2	Remembers which picture is own		
	Tells adult what picture is about		
	Selects own size/colour/type paper		
	Paints 'something' (e.g. person)		
	Uses 2–3 colours		
	Begins to control drips if trying to		
	Mixes own paint from pallet of powder and squeezy bottle of water		
1	Tells adult it is finished		
	Uses more than one colour		
	Makes circular brush strokes		
	Makes strokes on paper		
	Makes mark on paper		
	Accepts apron		
	Watches other children		

Playladders

Nursery area | MESSY

Play activity | GLUE TABLE

Comments

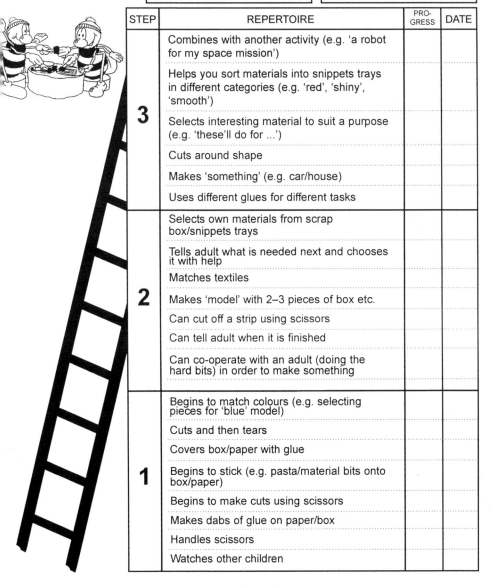

STEP	REPERTOIRE	PRO-GRESS	DATE
3	Combines with another activity (e.g. 'a robot for my space mission')		
	Helps you sort materials into snippets trays in different categories (e.g. 'red', 'shiny', 'smooth')		
	Selects interesting material to suit a purpose (e.g. 'these'll do for ...')		
	Cuts around shape		
	Makes 'something' (e.g. car/house)		
	Uses different glues for different tasks		
2	Selects own materials from scrap box/snippets trays		
	Tells adult what is needed next and chooses it with help		
	Matches textiles		
	Makes 'model' with 2–3 pieces of box etc.		
	Can cut off a strip using scissors		
	Can tell adult when it is finished		
	Can co-operate with an adult (doing the hard bits) in order to make something		
1	Begins to match colours (e.g. selecting pieces for 'blue' model)		
	Cuts and then tears		
	Covers box/paper with glue		
	Begins to stick (e.g. pasta/material bits onto box/paper)		
	Begins to make cuts using scissors		
	Makes dabs of glue on paper/box		
	Handles scissors		
	Watches other children		

Playladders

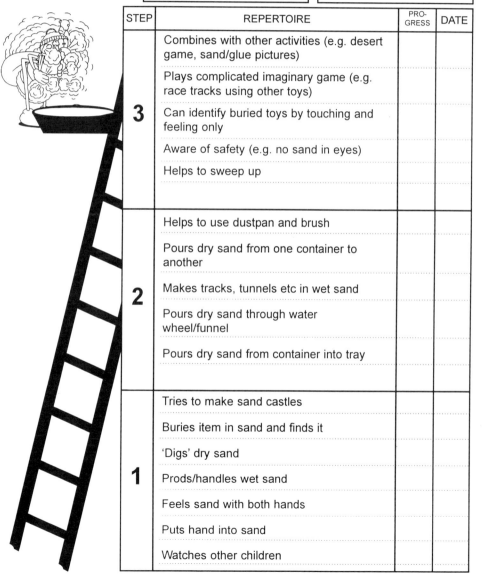

Nursery area	MESSY
Play activity	SAND TRAY

Comments

STEP	REPERTOIRE	PRO-GRESS	DATE
3	Combines with other activities (e.g. desert game, sand/glue pictures)		
	Plays complicated imaginary game (e.g. race tracks using other toys)		
	Can identify buried toys by touching and feeling only		
	Aware of safety (e.g. no sand in eyes)		
	Helps to sweep up		
2	Helps to use dustpan and brush		
	Pours dry sand from one container to another		
	Makes tracks, tunnels etc in wet sand		
	Pours dry sand through water wheel/funnel		
	Pours dry sand from container into tray		
1	Tries to make sand castles		
	Buries item in sand and finds it		
	'Digs' dry sand		
	Prods/handles wet sand		
	Feels sand with both hands		
	Puts hand into sand		
	Watches other children		

Playladders

Nursery area

Play activity

Comments

STEP	REPERTOIRE	PRO-GRESS	DATE
3			
2			
1			

Playladders

Nursery area

Play activity

Comments

STEP	REPERTOIRE	PRO-GRESS	DATE
3			
2			
1			